# GOD CARES FOR ME

## By Carolyn Muller Wolcott

### PICTURES BY LLOYD DOTTERER

New York          ABINGDON PRESS          Nashville

*Bong, bong, bong*
>went the big round clock.
>Betsy the dog jumped into her basket.
>Nero the cat curled up on his pillow.
>Bobbie hopped into bed.

It was nighttime.

Bobbie watched the stars through his window.
They twinkled in the sky.
Bobbie saw the moon like a big round ball.
It shone in Bobbie's yard
and made the trees look all silver.

"I like the nighttime,"
        Bobbie said to his mother.
"God planned it, didn't he?"

"Yes," said Mother.
    "He planned it
        so we can see the moon
        and watch the stars.
    He planned it
        so the puppy dogs in their baskets
        and the pussy cats on their pillows
        and the people in his world
        might go to sleep."

"Betsy and Nero are going to sleep," said Bobbie.
"Soon I'll be asleep, too.
Will God take care of me while I'm asleep?
Tell me real fast."

"Yes, indeed," said Mother.
    "God cares for you in the daytime
        and in the nighttime."

"How?" asked Bobbie.
    "How does God care for me?"

"God cares for you in many ways," Mother said.
    "He cares for you through people who help —
        through Mother and Daddy,
        through big sister Susan and Grandmommy,
        through friends who love you,
    And most of all through something inside you
        that helps you know
        what to do."

"Tell me about how God cares;
  About the people who help;
  About that something inside me,"
    begged Bobbie.
"Tell me before I go to sleep."


"All right," said Mother.
  "I'll sit beside you on the bed
    and tell you."

"God needs people
      to help him care for his world," Mother said.
"He needs mothers and daddies
      to live with boys and girls;
      to help them grow big and tall;
      to show them what is good;
      to put them to bed at night;
And, best of all,
      to love them."

Bobbie said,
   "I'm glad you and Daddy love me.
   I'm glad God needs mothers and daddies to help.
"Now tell me about big sister Susan and Grandmommy
      and our friends."

"God needs big sister Susan," said Mother,
  "and Grandmommy and our friends.
  He needs Susan
    to take your hand when you cross the street
    and tell you about the colors of the lights."

"I know about lights," laughed Bobbie.
  "Green means go, and red means stop."

"He needs Grandmommy," said Mother,
"to stay with you when we go out;
to sing you songs and tell you stories."

"I love Grandmommy," said Bobbie.
"She tells nice stories."

"He needs our friends," Mother said,
"To show us how to play together
and help us have happy times."

"I didn't know so many people helped God
      take care of me," said Bobbie.
"Now I want to know about that something
      inside me."


"God has put something in each of us
      so we can help him care for ourselves,"
      Mother told Bobbie.
"When you come at Mother's and Daddy's call,
      When you remember to take Susan's hand
      to cross the street,
      When you ride your bicycle on the sidewalk,
      When you take your nap in the afternoon —
"Then you are letting that something inside you
      help God take care of you."

"When I drink all my milk
and eat my vegetables,
Am I helping God take care of me?"
asked Bobbie.

"Indeed you are," said Mother.
"You are helping him make you
strong and tall."

"I'm glad there's something inside me
that helps when I let it," said Bobbie.
"Can I help God take care of other people, too?"

"Oh, yes," smiled Mother.
   "When you latch the gate
      so Debbie can't get out,
   When you take Susan's raincoat to school
      to keep her dry,
   When you help Judith remember not
      to run into the street —
"Then you are helping God take care of the
   people in his world."

*Bong, bong, bong*
        went the big clock again.
     Betsy the dog yawned and rolled over.
       Nero the cat purred and stretched.
      Bobbie pulled the covers up under his chin.
"Thank you, God, for taking care of me," he said.
  "Thank you for the people who help.
   Thank you for letting me help, too."

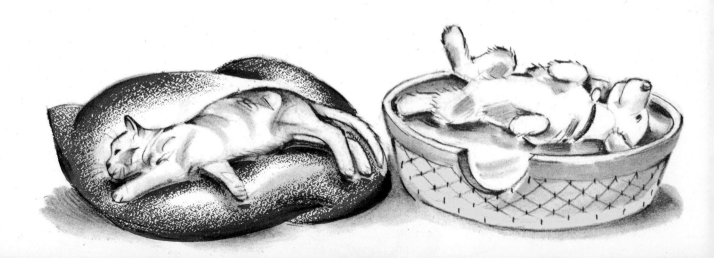

Bobbie was glad.
Bobbie was glad God cared for him.